HERE'S HEATHCLIFF by Geo Gately

AMERICA'S CRAZIEST CAT!

Volume II

© McNaught Synd., Inc.

THE BEST OF SUNDAY WITH HEATHCLIFF

HEATHCLIFF

ONE, TWO, THREE, AND YOU'RE OUT

TOR

A TOM DOHERTY ASSOCIATES BOOK

HERE'S HEATHCLIFF
Volume II

HEATHCLIFF
ONE, TWO, THREE, AND YOU'RE OUT

Copyright ©1981 by McNaught Syndicate, Inc.
All rights reserved
Published by arrangement with Windmill Books, Inc. and
Simon and Schuster, a division of Gulf and Western Corp.

A Tor Book

First printing, 1982

10 9 8 7 6 5 4 3 2 1

ISBN: 49-029-1

Printed in the United States of America

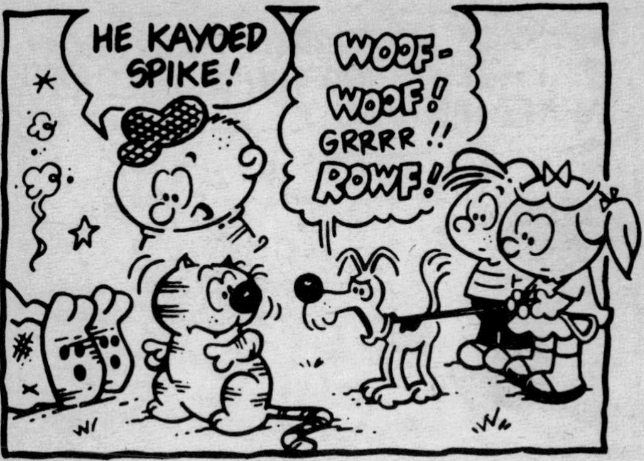
HE KAYOED SPIKE!
WOOF-WOOF! GRRRR!! ROWF!

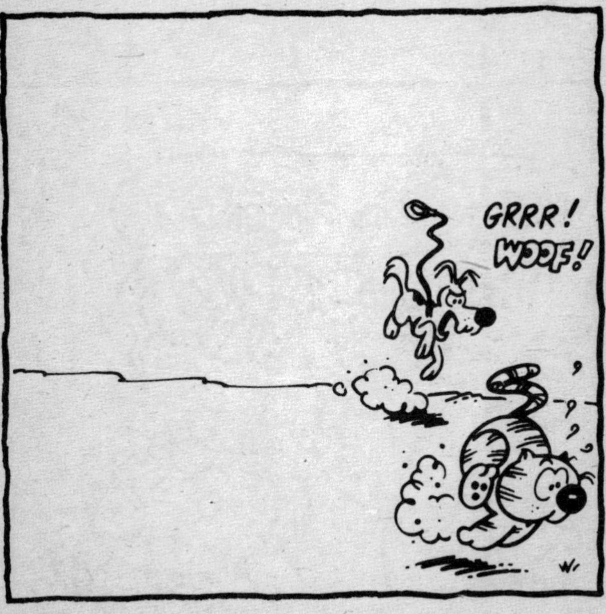
GRRR! WOOF!

8-1   1976
McNaught Synd., Inc.

HI!

BIDE-AWHILE ACRES
CATS BOARDED

AH, YES! - HEATHCLIFF ALWAYS ENJOYS HIS STAY WITH US!

KITTY KORNER!

YOU'VE HEARD THE EXPRESSION 'THE GRASS IS ALWAYS GREENER ETC'. MISS WHITNEY PAPE OF WATERTOWN, CONN., HAS FOUR CATS NAMED ASHES, BANDIT, SASSY AND SATEN, WHO DON'T GET ALONG.

ONE EVENING, ASHES SPOTTED SATEN'S DISH AND DECIDED IT LOOKED BETTER THAN HERS. SO SHE REACHED OUT HER PAW, SNAGGED THE EDGE OF THE BOWL WITH HER CLAW AND PULLED IT RIGHT OVER TO HERSELF, MUCH TO SATEN'S DISMAY!

KITTY KORNER!

BREAD LINE →

MRS. M.B. CLARK OF SAN DIEGO, CALIF., HAS A CAT NAMED 'MUDDY,' WHO SHE SAYS HAS A VERY HIGH MATERNAL INSTINCT!

ONE EVENING, AFTER MUDDY HAD BEEN FED SHE KEPT MEOWING AT THE DOOR 'TIL MRS. CLARK LOOKED... MUDDY HAD BROUGHT HOME A POOR UNDERNOURISHED CAT FOR SOME FOOD!... SO NOW, MRS. CLARK HAS AN EXTRA BOARDER. MUDDY HAS DONE THIS WITH OTHER CATS!

JUST A NEIGHBORLY VISIT...

by Geo Gately

KITTY KORNER!

SOME PEOPLE SAY YOU CAN'T TRAIN A CAT. MAYBE THAT'S BECAUSE CATS PREFER TO TRAIN PEOPLE!

MRS. RALPH MEIER OF DE KALB, ILL., SAYS WHEN HER CALICO, 'TIPPY,' WANTS TO COME IN, SHE CLIMBS UP ON THE RAILING AND LEANS AGAINST THE FRONT DOORBELL. IF NO ONE ANSWERS, SHE WAITS FIVE MINUTES AND RINGS AGAIN. ONE NIGHT, SHE RANG AT 4:00 A.M.! TIPPY LEARNED THE TRICK FROM HER SISTER AND NOW SHE'S TAUGHT IT TO HER SON!

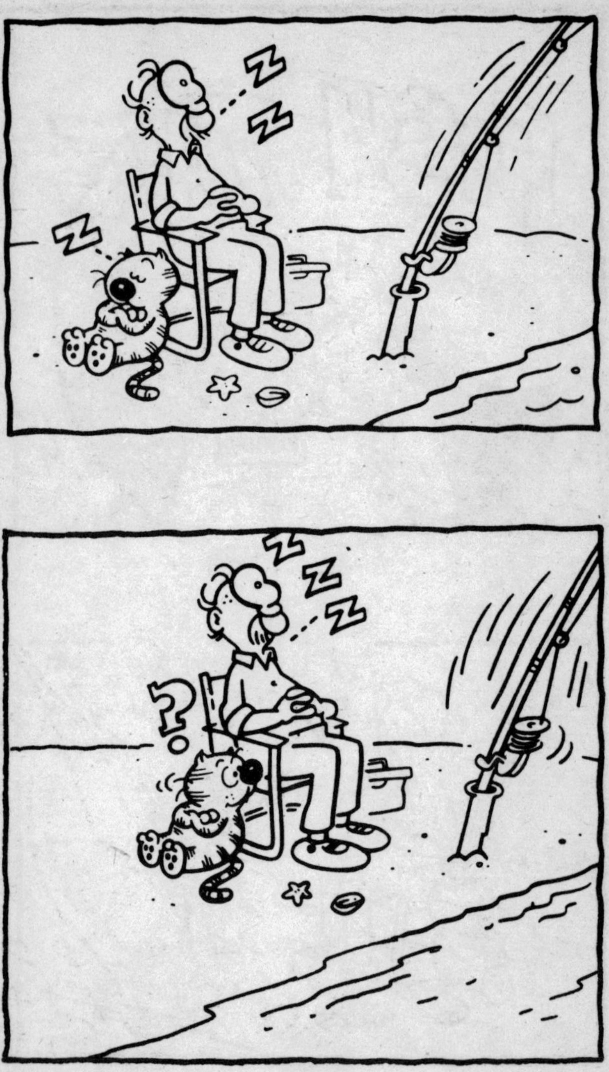
Z
Z
Z
Z
Z
Z
?

KITTY KORNER!

HOW'S *THIS* FOR A NAME?..........
'SUPERCALIFRAGILISTICXPYALADOCIA'!...THAT'S
HOW MARY MURPHY OF BRIDGEPORT, CONN., SPELLS
HER CAT'S NAME, OR 'SOUPY', FOR SHORT!

SOUPY LIKES COMPANY WHEN SHE EATS,
SO SHE MEOWS AT THE FRONT DOOR
TO GO OUT. WHEN MARY APPEARS SHE
HEADS FOR THE KITCHEN, HOPING
MARY WILL FOLLOW. AFTER 3 OR
4 TIMES, ONE OF THEM GIVES UP!

SPIKE HAD A TOOTHACHE

KITTY KORNER!

MRS. S. S. TAYLOR OF COLORADO SPRINGS, COLORADO, HAS A BLACK PERSIAN NAMED 'PRINCE'.... AND HE LIVES LIKE ONE! WHEN THE TAYLORS COME HOME, HE ROLLS OVER AND INSISTS ON HAVING HIS TUMMY SCRATCHED.

PRINCE ALSO LIKES TO SLEEP ON THEIR DAUGHTER'S BED. AND IF IT'S COLD, HE CRAWLS BETWEEN THE SHEETS. HE DOESN'T LIKE THE QUILT OR THE SPREAD. ONLY THE SHEETS WILL DO FOR A PRINCE!

CHIEF!...YOU'RE NOT GONNA BELIEVE THIS, BUT....

KITTY KORNER!

GAIL AND ARTHUR WHITE OF NEW ORLEANS, LA., LIVE IN A HOUSE WITH A BEAUTIFUL STAIRCASE AND 'PANDORA', THEIR BLACK CAT, LIKES TO SIT ON THE NEWEL POSTS.

WHENEVER GAIL OR ARTHUR PASSED BY, THEY WOULD SCRATCH HER EARS. NOW, SHE EXPECTS THIS, AND IF THEY FORGET, AS THEY GO BY, SHE CATCHES THEIR HANDS TO REMIND THEM TO PET HER!

PET STOP

A LITTLE CAT NAP

I WONDER WHAT CATS DREAM ABOUT?

MOM

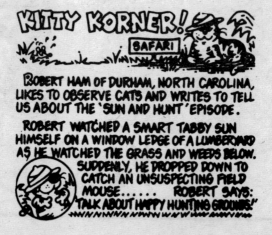

KITTY KORNER!

SAFARI

ROBERT HAM OF DURHAM, NORTH CAROLINA, LIKES TO OBSERVE CATS AND WRITES TO TELL US ABOUT THE 'SUN AND HUNT' EPISODE.

ROBERT WATCHED A SMART TABBY SUN HIMSELF ON A WINDOW LEDGE OF A LUMBERYARD AS HE WATCHED THE GRASS AND WEEDS BELOW. SUDDENLY, HE DROPPED DOWN TO CATCH AN UNSUSPECTING FIELD MOUSE...... ROBERT SAYS: "TALK ABOUT HAPPY HUNTING GROUNDS!"

STRANGE!...SOMEBODY CUT THE WIRES!!!

KITTY KORNER!

JULIE TREADWELL OF BATTLE CREEK, MICH., HAS A BLACK AND WHITE TOMCAT NAMED 'JUNIOR', WHO'S QUITE A GYMNAST!

JULIE SAYS THEY USED TO KEEP A BOX OF FACE TISSUES ON THE FLOOR BY THE TV, WHICH JUNIOR LIKED TO GRAB AND TEAR UP, LEAVING A TERRIBLE MESS. SO THEY PUT THE BOX UP ON THE COFFEE TABLE. NOW, WHENEVER JUNIOR WANTS ONE, HE JUMPS OVER THE TABLE AND ON HIS WAY, GRABS A TISSUE!

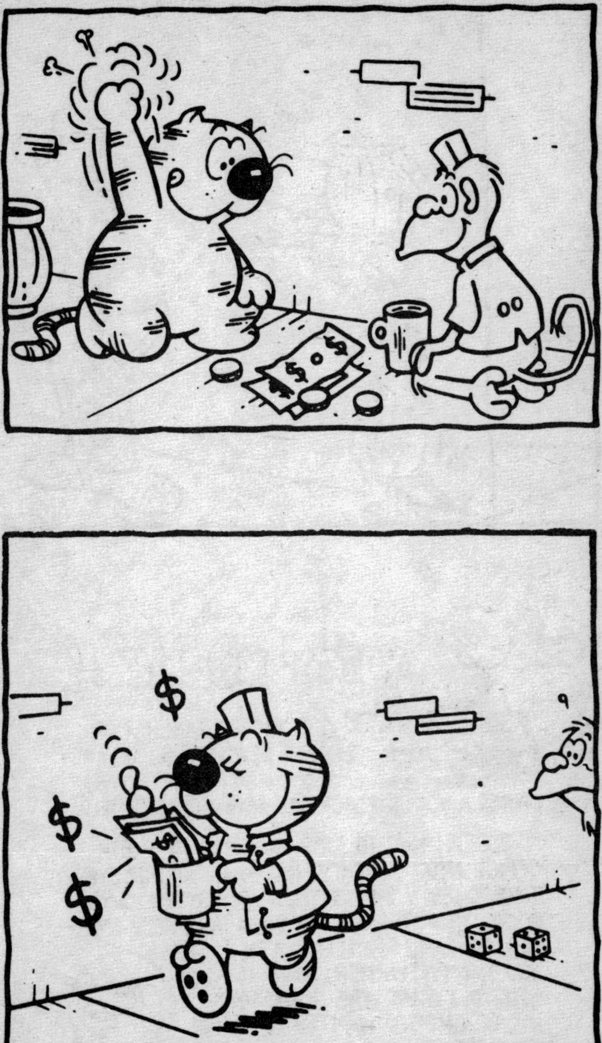

9-26 1976
McNaught Synd., Inc.

KITTY KORNER!

MR. JOSEPH GANCHER OF CONCORD, NEW HAMPSHIRE, WAS EMPLOYED BY A COUPLE WHO OWNED A YOUNG BLACK CAT NAMED 'CHESTERFIELD.'

JOSEPH HAD TO STOP WORKING IN THEIR OFFICE AND DO HIS TYPING AT HOME, FOR EVERY TIME 'CHESTY' HEARD THE TYPEWRITER KEYS GOING, HE'D JUMP ON THE DESK, AND KEEP WALKING BACK AND FORTH BETWEEN JOSEPH AND THE TYPEWRITER, AS IF HE WERE STUDYING WHAT WAS GOING ON! MAYBE CHESTY WANTED TO LEARN TO TYPE!!

KITTY KORNER!

MARIA HARMON OF MT. JULIET, TENNESSEE, HAS A NICE, BUT FUNNY GRAY AND WHITE OVER-GROWN KITTEN NAMED 'FRITZ'.

MARIA SAYS THEY HAVE A BIG SHAG RUG HANGING ON THE LIVING ROOM WALL. SOMETIMES FRITZ AND THEIR OTHER CAT, 'BOOBIE', LIKE TO CHASE EACH OTHER AROUND THE HOUSE. BOOBIE WILL CHASE FRITZ INTO THE LIVING ROOM AND FRITZ WILL CLIMB UP THE WALL-RUG, TURN AROUND AND RUN DOWN, DEFYING THE LAW OF GRAVITY!

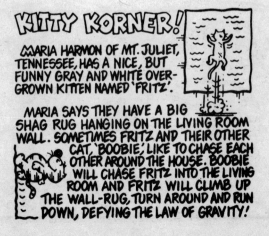

10-17 © 1976 McNaught Synd., Inc.

CITY PARK

BIG NIGHT ON THE TOWN?

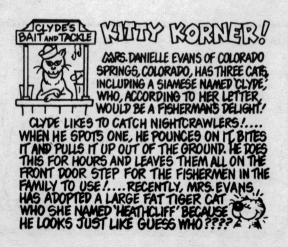

KITTY KORNER!

CLYDE'S BAIT AND TACKLE

MRS. DANIELLE EVANS OF COLORADO SPRINGS, COLORADO, HAS THREE CATS, INCLUDING A SIAMESE NAMED "CLYDE", WHO, ACCORDING TO HER LETTER, WOULD BE A FISHERMAN'S DELIGHT!

CLYDE LIKES TO CATCH NIGHTCRAWLERS!..... WHEN HE SPOTS ONE, HE POUNCES ON IT, BITES IT AND PULLS IT UP OUT OF THE GROUND. HE DOES THIS FOR HOURS AND LEAVES THEM ALL ON THE FRONT DOOR STEP FOR THE FISHERMEN IN THE FAMILY TO USE!..... RECENTLY, MRS. EVANS HAS ADOPTED A LARGE FAT TIGER CAT WHO SHE NAMED "HEATHCLIFF" BECAUSE HE LOOKS JUST LIKE GUESS WHO???

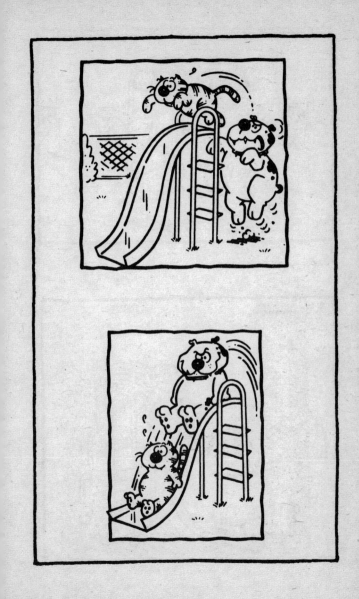

10-24   1976
McNaught Synd., Inc.

KITTY KORNER!

BUTTON UP!

DIANA AND AMY KAUFMAN OF BEVERLY HILLS, CALIF., HAVE A CAT NAMED 'PHILLIP' AND AN IRISH SETTER NAMED 'WILLY,' WHOSE BARK IS WORSE THAN HIS BITE!

IT SEEMS WILLY WILL KEEP BARKING AT PHILLIP, UNTIL PHILLIP GETS SICK AND TIRED OF LISTENING TO ALL THAT NOISE AND GIVES OUT WITH ONE REAL BIG HISS WHICH MAKES WILLY JUMP BACK WITH A CRY! WHAT AMAZES AMY AND DIANA IS WILLY IS FOUR TIMES THE SIZE OF PHILLIP BUT PHILLIP ALWAYS WINS!

1976
McNaught Synd., Inc.

KITTY KORNER!

MR. MARK R. HALSTEAD OF BRIDGEPORT, CONN., HAS A BIG FAT CAT NAMED 'TOTO,' WHO LIKES TO LOUNGE AROUND ON THE WINDOW SILL NEAR THEIR ORGAN.

ONE HOT SUMMER DAY, WHILE PLAYING THE SONG 'FOR ALL WE KNOW,' MARK NOTICED THAT TOTO KEPT PERFECT TIME TO THE BEAT OF THE MUSIC WITH HIS TAIL! HE DOES THIS WITH MANY OTHER SONGS TOO....

MAYBE MARK SHOULD RENAME TOTO...'HEPCAT'!

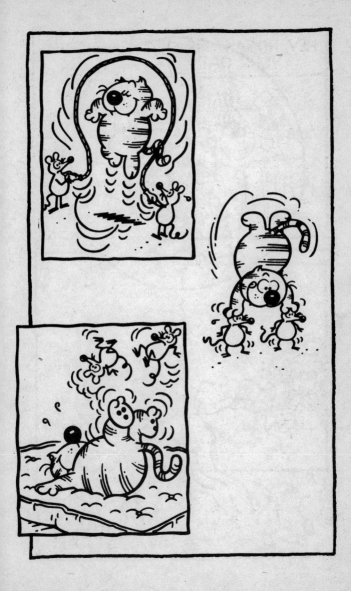

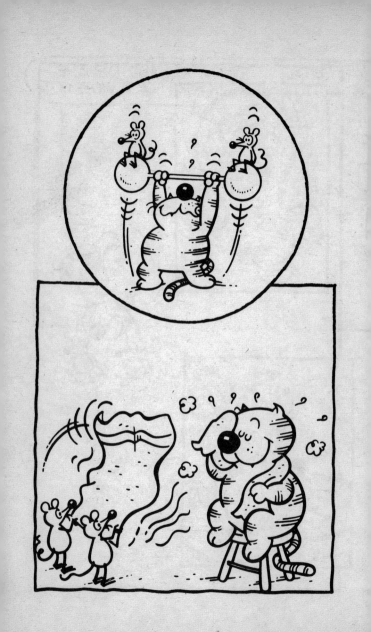

KITTY KORNER!

GRANT BISHOP OF OAK LAWN, ILLINOIS, WRITES ABOUT HIS FRIEND, SUE WOLFS, WHO OWNS A CAT NAMED 'TOM', WHO LIKES TO PLAY BASEBALL.

TOM LIKES TO PLAY CATCH WITH A BALL OF YARN. BUT THAT'S NOT ALL!....HE LIKES TO PLAY IT WHILE WEARING A BASEBALL CAP!..... *BATTER UP!!*

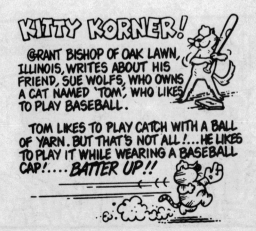

KITTY KORNER!

CAROL RICHARDSON OF WASILLA, ALASKA, OWNS A CALICO KITTEN NAMED "PUMKIN," WHO HAS SEVEN TOES ON BOTH FRONT PAWS, WHICH LOOK LIKE THUMBS.

THIS IS NOT UNUSUAL, EXCEPT THAT PUMKIN SUCKS HER THUMBS TO GO TO SLEEP!.... CAROL SAYS HER FRIENDS WON'T BELIEVE HER UNTIL THEY SEE FOR THEMSELVES.

TUNA-A-LA-HEATHCLIFF!

1976
McNaught
Syndicate, Inc.
-21

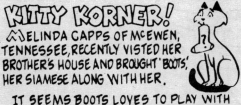

KITTY KORNER!

MELINDA CAPPS OF McEWEN, TENNESSEE, RECENTLY VISTED HER BROTHER'S HOUSE AND BROUGHT 'BOOTS,' HER SIAMESE ALONG WITH HER.

IT SEEMS BOOTS LOVES TO PLAY WITH SOCKS AND WHEN MELINDA TURNED HIM LOOSE, HE PULLED SEVEN SOCKS FROM UNDER THE BEDS, CHAIRS AND COUCH, NOW, MELINDA SAYS, HER BROTHER CAN MATCH UP ALL HIS PAIRS OF SOCKS! ... ONE QUESTION, MELINDA...WHAT WILL YOUR BROTHER DO WITH THE **SEVENTH** SOCK ???

AND HERE TO LAY THE CORNERSTONE...

WOT THE....?!

WHO'S THAT?!

WHERE'S THE MAYOR?

KITTY KORNER!

MRS. E. DRISCOLL OF TROUT-VILLE, VA., WRITES TO US ABOUT HER MOTHER, MRS. STEVEN PAULL, AND HER CAT, 'POOH' WHO SHE SAYS REALLY RUNS THE HOUSE.

POOH HAS MANY QUIRKS, BUT HER BEST TRICK IS HOPPING INTO A PLASTIC BASIN IN THE BOTTOM OF THE BATHTUB AND WATCHING THE WATER RUN INTO THE TUB FROM THE SAFETY OF HER SOMEWHAT UNSEA-WORTHY BARGE! — *LAND, HO!*

KITTY KORNER!

MR. DAVID M. ALPERT OF MERRITT ISLAND, FLORIDA, HAS YET TO SEE THE ELEVEN O'CLOCK EVENING NEWS ON TV.

AT EXACTLY ELEVEN, HIS PART SIAMESE, PART HIMALAYAN CAT COMES IN FROM THE ENCLOSED PATIO, MEOWS AND WALKS AROUND MR. ALPERT'S CHAIR, THEN GOES TO THE DOORWAY, POINTS BY SITTING DOWN FACING THE DOOR TO SHOW HE WANTS TO GO OUT FRONT. MR. ALPERT SAYS HE HASN'T MISSED A NIGHT!

KITTY KORNER!

VANITY, THY NAME IS 'STUBBY'! AT LEAST IT SEEMED THAT WAY TO MRS. W. J. PERRET, SR., WHO LIVES IN METAIRIE, LOUISIANA.

THEIR NEIGHBOR BOUGHT A NEW PICK-UP TRUCK AND EVERY TIME HE CAME HOME, STUBBY, THE PERRETS' CAT, RAN OVER AND WALKED AROUND THE TIRES. THEY THOUGHT HE WAS HUNTING SOMETHING, BUT ON CLOSER LOOK, FOUND STUBBY WAS ADMIRING HIMSELF IN THE HUB CAPS!.... SOMETIMES FOR AS LONG AS A HALF HOUR!

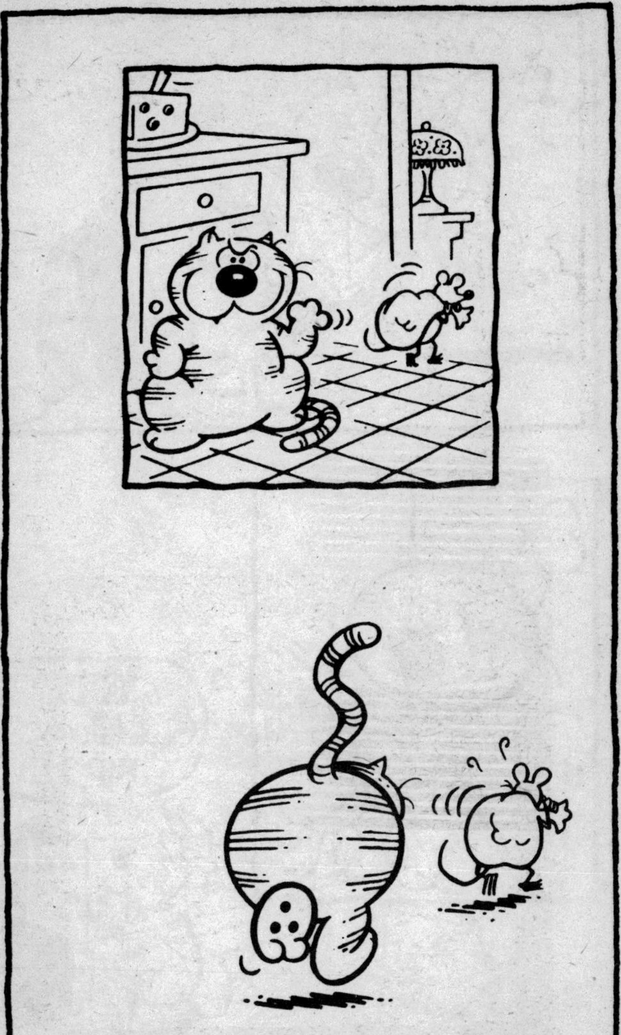

KITTY KORNER!

MRS. ANITA BUTWINSKI OF MAHWAH, N.J. CLAIMS HER TWO CATS, 'PRUFROCK' AND 'EZRA' ARE BOTH GREAT HEATHCLIFF FANS.

ONE AFTERNOON, MRS. BUTWINSKI WAS READING THE NEW HEATHCLIFF PAPERBACK BOOK OF CARTOONS TO HER NEPHEW, WHEN SHE NOTICED EZRA AND PRUFROCK (WHO ARE USUALLY IN SOME SORT OF MISCHIEF THIS TIME OF DAY) HAD JUMPED UP ON THE BACK OF THE CHAIR. THEY BOTH WERE SITTING QUIETLY, STARING DOWN AT THE BOOK AND LISTENING TO EVERY WORD!

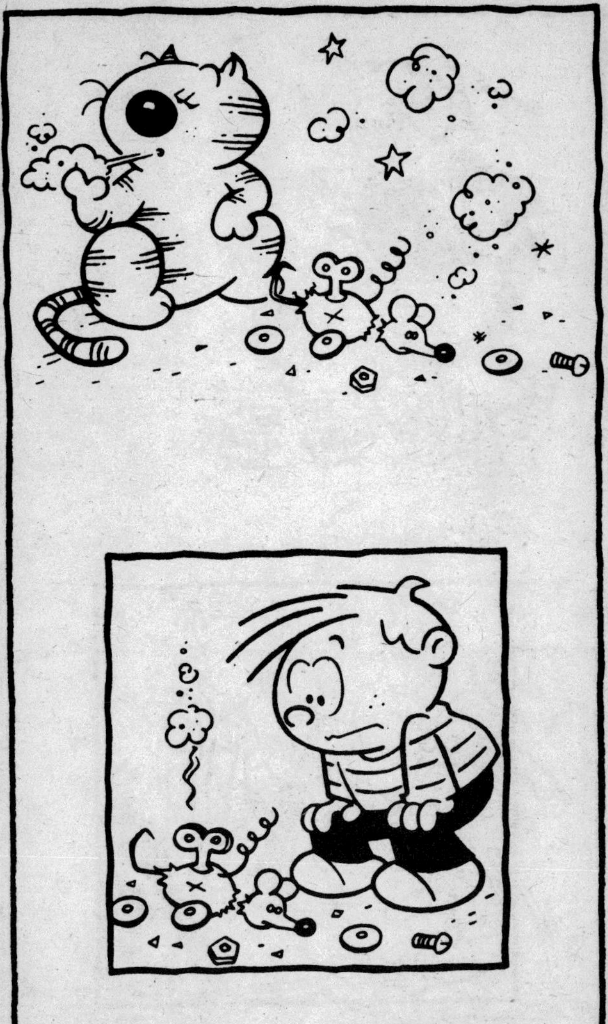

1976
McNaught Synd., Inc.

KITTY KORNER!

JAN AND JEFF LANDER OF POLO, ILLINOIS, SAY THEY THREW AWAY THEIR FLY SWATTER BACK WHEN THEIR 15 LB. STRIPED, LONG-HAIRED ALLEY CAT 'CASPER' WAS ONLY A KITTEN.

CASPER WILL BE SOUND ASLEEP, WHEN ONE EAR WILL DETECT A FLY IN THE HOUSE. HE WILL LIE THERE, THEN JUMP UP SIX FEET AND NAB THE FLY IN THE AIR! CASPER WILL PURSUE THEM ALL OVER THE HOUSE UNTIL HE IS SUCCESSFUL.

THE TRY-OUT

by Geg Gately

KITTY KORNER!

MR. ROBERT C. CUSHNIE OF LOS ANGELES, CALIF., WROTE ABOUT 'SCATTER', HIS DAUGHTER SYLVIA'S CAT, WHO COMES RUNNING HOME FROM ANY PLACE AT TWO LOUD CLAPS OF THE HANDS.

SCATTER CAN DO MANY THINGS, BUT HER MOST UNUSUAL ANTIC IS WHEN SHE GOES FROM ROOM TO ROOM, SHE STANDS UP AND PUSHES THE DOORS OPEN AND ON HER WAY BACK, SHE REACHES UNDER THE DOORS AND PULLS THEM OPEN AGAIN!

AS MR. CUSHNIE SAYS: "THAT'S SCATTER!"

KITTY KORNER!

KIM PRAKOPCHUK OF DAUPHIN, MANITOBA, CANADA, HAS A SIAMESE NAMED CLEO AND A WHITE STRAY NAMED SAM. CLEO REFUSES TO FALL ASLEEP AND MEONS UNTIL GIVEN A DRINK OF WATER.

THE FUNNIEST ONE IS SAM. IF KIM AND A MEMBER OF HER FAMILY LIE BESIDE HIM AND THEY TALK TOO MUCH, SAM LIFTS HIS PAW AND PLACES IT OVER THEIR MOUTH, AS IF TO SAY: "QUIET, I'M RESTING!"

IT LOOKS LIKE THERE'S BEEN AN EVICTION!

1977
McNaught Synd Inc

KITTY KORNER!

JOSEPH W. TURNER OF NEW ORLEANS, LA., OVERHEARD THE FOLLOWING CONVERSATION BETWEEN TWO BROTHERS.

THE LITTLE BROTHER (AGE 9) ASKED IF HE COULD BRING HOME A KITTEN THAT WAS HALF SIAMESE. JUMPING AT THE OPPORTUNITY TO SHOW HIS SUPERIOR KNOWLEDGE, THE BIG BROTHER (AGE 13) RETORTED: "DON'T BE STUPID! IF YOU SEPARATE SIAMESE KITTENS, BOTH OF THEM WILL DIE!"